# THE
# Just Seventeen
# QUIZ BOOK

## ANITA NAIK

Hodder
Children's
Books

a division of Hodder Headline

'Just Seventeen' is a trademark of EMP,
Scriptor Court,
155 Farringdon Road,
London, EC1R

Cover artwork by Nick Sharratt

Published by Hodder & Stoughton Children's Books 1994

10 9 8 7 6 5 4 3

ISBN 0 340 60164 7

Printed and bound in Great Britain by
The Guernsey Press Co. Ltd, Guernsey, Channel Islands

Hodder Children's Books
A division of Hodder Headline
338 Euston Road
London NW1 3BH

# THE Just Seventeen QUIZ BOOK

ANITA NAIK

# contents

contents

LEARNING about yourself

# LEARNING about
## yourself

★ ★ ★ ★ ★

Hands up who hasn't looked at themselves
and thought, "Yuck, I hate myself. I hate my
life and I don't know what to do about it".
Well, if you haven't you're very lucky. I know
from experience that many of my friends, me
included, felt very much this way through
much of our teenage years.

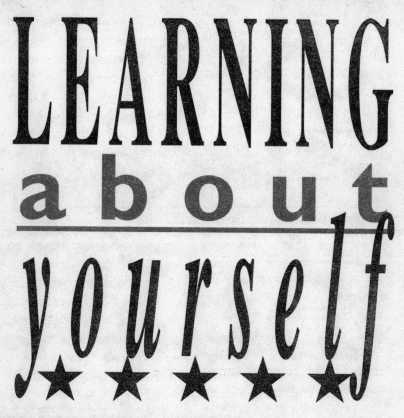

8

★ ★ ★ ★ ★

*L*ife to me back then seemed pretty much a boring endless repetition of getting up - going to school - coming home - watching TV- eating dinner- homework - and bed. I'd sit in my bedroom and work out how many more years I'd have to live like this and then get depressed with the answer.

If only I knew back then what I know now. That leading a repetitive life doesn't mean you're a boring person, and in between all the things you have to do is a lot of time to do the things you want to do. Discovering who you are and becoming the person you want to be is an exciting process, so don't waste any time wishing away these years.

After all, no matter what you end up doing for a living, life can end up feeling repetitive, boring and just plain dull. This has nothing to do with the job we do, the friends we have or even the school we go to. It's got far more to do with the way we choose to live our lives.

Someone once said, 'A life lived in fear is a life half lived'. But you don't need to live this way. Your life doesn't need to be boring because you're too afraid to go after what you want. There are plenty of people around who will put a damper on your dreams and tell you that girls from your background can't become mega stars, or brain surgeons. Don't listen to them. You can be whoever and whatever you want.

Learn to utilise the spare time you have. If you want to make films, watch videos and mark down bits you like and why. If you want to write then make sure you read a lot and write whenever you feel like it. If you want to travel the world, check out the library and see what charities need help abroad. There's a way to anything you want as long as you believe you can do it.

If you have no idea what you want to be or where you want to go, then don't panic. There's no rush, but don't waste your spare time. Often what we choose to do out of pleasure

9

can be a good indicator of what we want to do with our lives. If you play lots of sport why not go for a sporty career? If you like shopping, what about a life in fashion? The list of things you can choose to do are endless. But don't forget, nothing you choose to do is ever written in stone. You can change your mind any time you want and pick something different.

Of course, there are going to be times when we don't like ourselves and the things we do. In fact, there are times when I positively hate myself and wish I was someone else. But, I try not to get too down about it because, in my heart, I know we all get fed up sometimes and wish we were someone else.

Supermodel Cindy Crawford, says she spent much of her teenage years wishing she didn't have her now famous mole and was someone else. As did Madonna and now look where she is. If you really hate yourself then write down a list of good and bad things about yourself. Concentrate more on the good points you have (and everyone has them), and capitalise on them.

If at any time you feel life really isn't worth living then you must talk to someone about your fears. Talking your problems through can ease your worries because it helps you to see that there are people who not only feel the same way as you, but can help as well.

Remember, no matter what age you are, we're all scared of the future and what it might or might not hold for us. The important thing is not to live in the future but the present. Make the best out of what you're doing now and the future will take care of itself.

★ ★ ★ ★ ★ ★ ★

# are you too nice?

★ ★ ★ ★ ★ ★ ★ •

**Being nice can get you an awful long way in life – but just how far are you willing to take it? Would you give your last pound to some deserving soul or keep it in your pocket?**

★ ★ ★ ★ ★

**1** **You've just spent the evening with a new boyfriend. He has treated you to a really flash evening. You don't fancy him but he's really keen on you. He asks you out again, what do you say?**

☐ **a** No way – you're boring, I'd rather stay in and chat to the potted plant.

☐ **b** Yes – you feel bad because he really likes you and you don't want to hurt him.

☐ **c** I don't want a boyfriend right now so let's be friends.

**2** **You're out babysitting and the parents arrive back an hour late, making you late to meet your friends. What do you do?**

☐ **a** Throw a tantrum and demand they compensate you for their lateness.

☐ **b** Nothing, they probably couldn't help it and you need the job.

☐ **c** Be a bit off with them and hope they notice.

**3** **Your friend hasn't done her homework and is worried she's going to be caught. She asks to copy yours. What do you do?**

☐ **a** Copy it for her.

☐ **b** Offer to help her out but don't let her copy your work.

☐ **c** Laugh and say, 'you're going to get in trouble'.

**4** **Your sister is about to go on a hot date but has nothing to wear. You know she really**

★ ★ ★ ★ ★

**wants to wear your new black dress but you haven't even worn it yet. What would you do?**

- ☐ **a** Put it on and pretend it's your new couch potato outfit.
- ☐ **b** Hide it but offer to lend her something else.
- ☐ **c** Give it to her, after all you don't have a hot date.

## 5 You're on the bus and feeling really tired when someone asks you for your seat. They look perfectly capable of standing up but what do you do?

- ☐ **a** You're so embarrassed you give it up immediately and stand there for the rest of the journey with a red face.
- ☐ **b** Say 'only if you give me some of my fare back'.
- ☐ **c** Say you're getting off in two stops, and ask them to wait.

## 6 A friend borrowed five pounds two months ago and still hasn't returned it. You really need it back what do you do?

- ☐ **a** Complain that you're really short of cash and then send the heavies out to get it.
- ☐ **b** Feel bad about asking for it, so borrow off your mum instead.
- ☐ **c** Ask her for it.

## 7 Your best friend returns a jacket she borrowed from you with a huge stain on it. What do you say?

- ☐ **a** Nothing, but vow never to lend her anything again.

★ ★ ★ ★ ★

**b** Nothing, you might have given it to her in that condition.

**c** 'What the hell is this. I hope you're going to pay for it!'

## 8 A woman queue jumps at the supermarket. You're really annoyed because you've been waiting for fifteen minutes to pay. What do you do?

**a** Say in a very loud voice, 'Do you mind!' and then throw a baked bean can at her.

**b** Shrug it off, after all you've done it before.

**c** Get really annoyed about it but say nothing to anyone.

## 9 You're just about to leave and meet a friend when she calls up and says her boyfriend's asked her out and would you mind if she cancelled. What do you say?

**a** 'Oh! That's fine I didn't want to go out any way.'

**b** Have a moan at her but let her off because you might want to do it one day.

**c** Tell her you never want to see her again.

## 10 You and your friend fancy the same guy but he asks you out. What do you do?

**a** Say no, because you don't want her to be hurt.

**b** Say yes, but speak to her about it first.

**c** Say yes, after all, all's fair in love and war.

14

★ ★ ★ ★ ★

**1** a 0   b 10   c 5

**2** a 0   b 10   c 5

**3** a 10   b 5   c 0

**4** a 0   b 5   c 10

**5** a 10   b 0   c 5

**6** a 5   b 10   c 0

**7** a 5   b 0   c 10

**8** a 10   b 5   c 0

**9** a 0   b 5   c 10

**10** a 10   b 5   c 0

scores

15

### 0 – 40

Well, no-one's ever going to take advantage of you, are they? You're positively ruthless and what's more you're darn proud of it. But do us all a favour and soften up a bit. Walking around being nasty to everyone may get you what you want, but it won't win you any friends, and what's more it will get you a pretty bad reputation. Ease up and you'll find life doesn't need to be one long battle.

### 45 – 75

You've got things pretty sussed haven't you? You know when to be nice and when to put your foot down. No-one will ever peg you as a doormat because you've got the balance right. You know what you want and you're strong enough to go for it. You've probably got tonnes of friends who rush to you for advice and help and so they should.

### 80 – 100

You're so nice, you make Mother Theresa look positively nasty. But I bet you spend a fair bit of your time wondering why people walk all over you. It's all fair and well to be nice, but don't let people take advantage of you. Stand up for yourself now and again; don't be a human doormat. After all, it's okay to be mad and angry sometimes, and it's okay to say no when you don't want to do something.

# how
# ADVENTUROUS
# *are*
# *you?*

★ ★ ★ ★ ★

Do you reckon you could be the female version of Indiana Jones, pursuing hidden treasure and fighting for what you want? Or would you rather sit at home with a bar of chocolate, watch TV and dream of what you could do?

**1** Your friends all fancy going on a diving holiday. You'd love to go but the trouble is you're scared of water. What would you do?

☐ **a** Tell them the truth and ask one of them to teach you how to swim.
☐ **b** Agree and have secret swimming lessons every day till you go.
☐ **c** Say no and comment on what a waste of money it all seems.

**2** You really fancy a boy who works in your local shop. You know he quite likes you but he's too shy to talk to you. Would you ask him out?

☐ **a** No way! What if he said no, you couldn't stand the rejection, the humiliation, the general agony of it all.
☐ **b** Yes, why not, it's better to know where you stand than waste time on him if he's not interested.
☐ **c** Eventually but not until you've found out everything you can about him, including what sort of girls he likes.

**3** Friends of your parents invite you over to America for the summer. The trouble is you don't know them and their family. Would you go?

☐ **a** Yes, why not! After all Brad Pitt lives over there.
☐ **b** No. What if you hated them or they hated you and you couldn't get home.
☐ **c** Say yes, but agree to go for only two weeks.

**4** You're going on a 10 mile country hike and you don't have to wear school uniform. This is your chance to impress your mates with your

**wonderful sense of style. What do you wear?**

- [ ] **a** Your 6" stilettos, micro mini and tight, short t-shirt – who cares if you can hardly walk, you're guaranteed to grab everyone's attention.
- [ ] **b** Jeans, t-shirt, ruck sack and hiking boots – you can be stylish in anything you wear.
- [ ] **c** Your school uniform – what's the point of dressing up just to hike 10 miles across country?.

## 5 Your school has entered you for a debating competition. You don't think you're good enough but can't get out of it. What do you do on the day?

- [ ] **a** Get your mum to ring in and say you're ill and have lost your voice.
- [ ] **b** Take a deep breath and just go for it.
- [ ] **c** Worry all day, try to get a friend to take your place and then do it anyway.

## 6 You and your friend have been invited to the party of a boy you really fancy. At the last minute she is struck down with an illness. Would you still go?

- [ ] **a** No way. You'd be far too nervous to talk to anyone there, least of all him and you don't want to be stuck in a corner all night.
- [ ] **b** Yes, but spend most of the night talking to the furniture.
- [ ] **c** Yes and be the life and soul of the party.

## 7 You order some food in a restaurant. It comes out cold. Would you complain?

**a** It depends how posh the restaurant is.

**b** Yes, because you are paying for it and you may end up getting a discount.

**c** No, you don't like to make a fuss.

## 8 You're out shopping when you see your favourite singer out with a friend, would you go up and speak to him?

**a** Yes, you'd talk to him, kiss him and generally cling to his leg till he took you home with him

**b** Yes, but only if you had a friend with you for moral support.

**c** No way, you're far too nervous and you know you'd make a fool out of yourself.

## 9 You've got a really nice voice and would love to be a singer. At a family wedding, your grandmother announces you are going to sing. What would you do?

**a** Duck under the nearest table and hope no-one finds you.

**b** Cringe, go bright red and mumble a few lines of 'I Will Always Love You'.

**c** Grab the microphone and belt out all your best numbers.

## 10 You've just broken up with the boy of your dreams and are thoroughly heartbroken. How do you feel about love now?

**a** You're never going to try it again – it hurts too much.

**b** It's better to have loved and lost then never to have loved at all.

**c** It hurts but you want to give it another try some day.

# scores

1. a 10    b 5    c 0
2. a 0    b 10    c 5
3. a 5    b 10    c 0
4. a 10    b 5    c 0
5. a 0    b 10    c 5
6. a 0    b 5    c 10
7. a 5    b 10    c 0
8. a 10    b 5    c 0
9. a 0    b 5    c 10
10. a 0    b 10    c 5

21

## 0 – 25

What are you so afraid of? The chances are it's failure, but believe me, there's no such thing as failing. If you always judge yourself in this way, then it's going to stop you from doing what you want. You don't have to be perfect in everything you do, in fact there's no such thing as perfection. Realise that it really doesn't matter if you fall on your bottom now and again, as long as you go for what you want.

## 30 – 65

Well, you've nearly got it. You've got the guts to stand up and do what you want but you're still too afraid of what other people think. But as long as you don't step all over people, they'll support you in whatever you do. So what if you want to be a popstar, an Oscar-winning actress or even an astronaut, don't be ashamed of your dreams. Tell people about them and make them come true by believing you can really do it.

## 70 – 100

Indiana Jones watch out! Phew, you're the sort of girl who'll not only climb mountains but move them as well. Congratulations, you may not know what you want from life but you're sure going to give everything your best shot until you find out. And you've got it sussed girl, it isn't what you end up with at the end of the adventure that's important, it's the adventure itself that makes life worthwhile.

# WE all need friends

> > > > >

You can get by without most things in life: love comes and goes; careers change and families disperse. But if you have no friends life can be tough. The good thing about friends is that if you look after them, nurture them and treat them the way you, yourself expect to be treated, they can last forever.

24

✳ ✳ ✳ ✳ ✳ ✳ ✳ ✳ ✳ ✳ ✳ ✳ ✳ ✳

Some people are lucky they have lots of friends, others may only want a few and some prefer just to have one. Whatever your preference, don't take them for granted.

My friends have been a lifesaver on many occasions. There's the one who sat with me all night when my boyfriend broke up with me, another who drove thirty miles to pick me up when my car broke down and the one who makes me laugh whenever I cry. I couldn't live without them and wouldn't want to.

Best friends are all well and good, but try not to put all your eggs into one basket and be cliquey. There's nothing more off putting than two girls who sneak off together all the time and refuse to mix with anyone else. If this sounds like you, ask yourself what you'd do if your best friend moved or you had a fight with her? It's far more healthy to have lots of different friends for different things. After all, you can still be

best friends and have other friends too.

Many a good friendship has been destroyed because of a boyfriend. But boys may come and go while a friend can last a lifetime. It's easy in the first throes of love to get carried away and ignore your friends. But if you start dumping them because your boyfriend turns up unexpectedly, then don't expect them to be there when you need a shoulder to cry on.

If you have trouble making friends, there are some easy ways to do it. For a start make sure you walk around looking cheerful and happy. No-one fancies making friends with someone who never smiles. Then work out who you want to be friends with and why. It's tempting to go for the most popular girl but what's the point if you've got nothing in common with her. Pick someone who has similar interests to you and then make an effort to get involved in things outside of school, that she may be

25

interested in as well. Not only will this give you a chance to meet new people but it also gives you something to talk about besides school.

If you're quite shy and never know what to say in a conversation a good tip to remember is to ask questions. People love to talk about themselves and when they do, try not to panic about what to say next. Instead, concentrate on what they are saying and make sure your questions follow on.

It's also important to realise that if you don't like yourself how can you expect anyone else to like you. Try not to be the sort of person who always puts themselves down. Concentrate instead on your good points and believe in yourself. If you think you're a bad or nasty person, so will other people. Likewise believing you're charming and nice will make people want to be with you.

Friendship takes work like anything else. It means keeping in contact when you're busy, writing letters if you're far away, telephoning just for a chat and being there when someone needs you. If you're not willing to take the bad times with the good then you need to ask yourself whether or not you really deserve a friend.

Of course, as we get older, all our relationships change and friendships are no different. As you start deciding what you want to do and where you want to go, you may find that you are leaving some of your friends behind. But this doesn't mean you have to lose their friendship. If you're willing to accept that things in your life have moved and your friendship is changing form, you can still remain friends for years and years to come.

# IS SHE really *your best* *friend?*

Is she really your best friend? Does she have your interests at heart or is she about to stab you in the back? ➤

27

> > > > > > > >

**1** You have a hot date and want to look special. You ask your best friend for advice. What does she say?

- [ ] **a** 'For starters you need to go on a diet and then get your hair cut, then buy some new clothes etc . . .'
- [ ] **b** 'You look great in everything, so don't worry.'
- [ ] **c** 'Let's go shopping and see what we can find.'

**2** Does your best friend ever flirt with your boyfriend?

- [ ] **a** Only for a joke.
- [ ] **b** Never.
- [ ] **c** All the time.

**3** You tell your best friend a painful secret about yourself. Is she likely to tell anyone about it?

- [ ] **a** Yes, but only by accident.
- [ ] **b** Yes, she likes gossiping.
- [ ] **c** No, she's totally trustworthy.

**4** You have a fight with your boyfriend. Whose side would your friend take?

- [ ] **a** Yours, of course.
- [ ] **b** She'd listen to the argument and then decide.
- [ ] **c** Your boyfriend's.

## 5 You go out for a girl's night, but when you're out your friend gets chatted up. Would she . . .

- [ ] **a** Go off with the boy and leave you by yourself.
- [ ] **b** Introduce you to his friend.
- [ ] **c** Arrange to meet him the next day.

## 6 When you talk about something does your friend . . .

- [ ] **a** Change the subject when you go on too long.
- [ ] **b** Listen intently to what you're saying.
- [ ] **c** Yawn loudly and interrupt you.

## 7 Has your best friend ever ditched you as soon as a boy came on the scene?

- [ ] **a** All the time.
- [ ] **b** Only once.
- [ ] **c** Never.

## 8 You're out at a party and you see your ex with his new girlfriend. What does your best friend do?

- [ ] **a** Suggest you both go somewhere else.
- [ ] **b** Constantly tell you how pretty and attractive she is.
- [ ] **c** Tell you all the faults his new girlfriend has.

## 9 You have a dreadful new haircut and hate it. What does your best friend do?

- [ ] **a** Buy you a hat.
- [ ] **b** Laugh every time she sees you.
- [ ] **c** Help you think of ways to make it look better.

## 10 Your boyfriend ditches you and leaves you broken-hearted. You call up your friend. What would she do?

- [ ] **a** Buy a box of Kleenex and rush round to comfort you.
- [ ] **b** Say 'Never mind, he was a creep anyway. Let's go out and look for a new one.'
- [ ] **c** Try and date your boyfriend.

**1**  a 0      b 10      c 5

**2**  a 5      b 0       c 10

**3**  a 5      b 0       c 10

**4**  a 10     b 5       c 0

**5**  a 0      b 5       c 10

**6**  a 5      b 10      c 0

**7**  a 0      b 5       c 10

**8**  a 10     b 0       c 5

**9**  a 5      b 0       c 10

**10** a 10     b 5       c 0

Scores

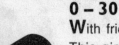

### 0 – 30

With friends like these who needs enemies? This girl really isn't your friend. She takes advantage of you, manipulates situations and will stab you in the back the minute you turn round. Why are you friends with her? Do yourself a massive favour and get a real friend. Real friends are happy for you when you achieve something and comforting when you're down. This girl is far too insecure to have a friend like you and won't ever do you any favours. Let her sort herself out and then see if she's worth being friends with.

### 35 – 70

You and your friend have got a pretty good thing going. It's a give and take, pretty balanced relationship. But don't be afraid to talk things out when you're upset with each other. After all, it's okay to admit you both sometimes get jealous of each other and don't always want to see each other. It doesn't mean you're any the less friends. Be a bit more honest with each other about what you both want and your friendship may last years.

### 75 – 100

Lucky you, you've got a friend in a million. She'll never let you down, flirt with your boyfriend or laugh when someone breaks your heart. She'll give you a helping hand whenever you need it and what's more she'll always be on your side. What more could you ask for? Fancy lending her to me?

# HOW GOOD a friend are YOU?

Would you walk a million miles to see a friend in trouble? Well, maybe not that far but how good a mate do you really think you are? Try this quiz and find out.

33

# 1 Your friend calls you up at 8 pm in tears because she can't study for a test. You've got a date that night, what would you do?

- [ ] **a** Tell her it serves her right for cramming so late.
- [ ] **b** Ditch your date and go round and help her.
- [ ] **c** Give her as much help as you can on the phone and tell her you'll help her on the way to school.

# 2 Your best friend's boyfriend is two-timing her. Would you tell her?

- [ ] **a** Yes, you'd want to be told if it was happening to you.
- [ ] **b** No, you don't want to upset her.
- [ ] **c** No, it's none of your business.

# 3 You're at your friend's house and while she's on the phone you spot her diary. Would you read it?

- [ ] **a** Yes, you can't help it – you're nosy.
- [ ] **b** Feel tempted but know you couldn't handle the guilt.
- [ ] **c** No, you'd hate it if she did it to you.

# 4 Your friend tells you a secret and you accidentally blab it about. Would you confess before she finds out?

- **a** Yes, because you don't want her to be even madder at you.
- **b** No, and plead ignorance when she confronts you.
- **c** Yes, but say you heard someone else say it first.

## 5 Your best friend's ex asks you out. You fancy him but know she still has a thing about him. What would you do?

- **a** Say yes because she doesn't own him.
- **b** Tell her before you make a decision.
- **c** Turn him down. You couldn't hurt her feelings.

## 6 Your best friend has got involved in drugs. You know she is getting deeper into trouble but doesn't want her parents to know. What would you do?

- **a** Tell her parents, you know she needs help.
- **b** Talk to her and suggest she gets help.
- **c** Nothing, you don't want to destroy her trust.

## 7 Her boyfriend makes a pass at you when she's not around. Would you tell her?

- **a** It depends on how long they had been going out.
- **b** No way, you don't want to lose her friendship.
- **c** Yes, because he's a creep and doesn't deserve her.

**8** Your friend wants to borrow your leather jacket but you don't want to lend it to anyone. What do you say?

- [ ] **a** Sorry, but I don't want to lend it out.
- [ ] **b** Yes, of course.
- [ ] **c** Buy your own.

**9** You have arranged to go out for your friend's birthday but at the same time you get given one ticket for your favourite band's concert. What do you do?

- [ ] **a** Go to the concert, you know she'll understand.
- [ ] **b** Give the ticket away, you can always go next year.
- [ ] **c** Ask her what you should do.

**10** You win two tickets to go to Paris for the weekend, who would you take?

- [ ] **a** Your friend, because you know you'll have a brilliant time.
- [ ] **b** Your boyfriend.
- [ ] **c** Whoever begs the most for the ticket.

| | | | | | |
|---|---|---|---|---|---|
| 1 | a 0 | | b 10 | | c 5 |
| 2 | a 10 | | b 5 | | c 0 |
| 3 | a 0 | | b 5 | | c 10 |
| 4 | a 10 | | b 0 | | c 5 |
| 5 | a 0 | | b 5 | | c 10 |
| 6 | a 10 | | b 5 | | c 0 |
| 7 | a 5 | | b 0 | | c 10 |
| 8 | a 10 | | b 5 | | c 0 |
| 9 | a 0 | | b 10 | | c 5 |
| 10 | a 10 | | b 5 | | c 0 |

### 0 – 35

Mmm . . . Call yourself a friend do you? Who are you trying to kid. Friendship is something that takes work and commitment. The only commitment you seem to have is to yourself. Have you ever wondered why your friends wander off after a while? Well, it's because they are pretty fed up with the way you always put yourself first. Of course, there's nothing wrong with doing what you want, but not at the expense of other people's feelings. If you want to be a good friend think about your friend for a change and what's good for her.

### 40 – 65

No doubt you have a lot of friends but may be not one best friend. If you really want a best friend you need to spend a bit more time thinking about what the other person needs and not just you. Of course, you may be very happy not to have to do this and good on you if you feel this way because best friends are the be all and end and all of life. If you have got a best friend, then perhaps you need to be a bit more honest with each other about what annoys you and what doesn't.

### 70 – 100

Well, you're a friend in a million aren't you? You've discovered that what makes your friend happy makes you happy as well. You're lucky because I bet she's just as good a friend to you as you are to her. The two of you will go far together. Congratulations.

*results*

38

ABOUT YOUR family

# ABOUT your family

If you come from a supportive family then you're very lucky. If you have siblings you get on with and a mother and father who love each other then you're luckier still. However, in truth, the majority of families aren't made up of the standard mother, father, two siblings and a dog stereotype the adverts would have us believe.

40

Many of us are growing up with one parent, step-parents and a multitude of step-brothers and sisters.

The important thing to remember is that all families fight and argue. It's perfectly natural and normal. In fact it would be near impossible to live with someone day in and day out for eighteen years without disagreeing now and then. Of course, it's hard when you see your family every day, not to take them for granted and get annoyed everytime they get in your way. But a little compromise can go a long, long way.

Perhaps your parents don't get on with your friends/boyfriend. If this is the case, you have to ask yourself if any of their reasons have any ring of truth to them. If they really don't then remind yourself that you probably don't like all of their friends, so why should they like all of yours. If they are too over-protective, always on your case about homework, or give you no privacy, then you need to talk to them and tell them why they are making you unhappy. This is hard because we grow up with the notion that are parents know everything, do everything right and have the answers to the world's problems, but of course they don't. They are human beings like you and me, and what's more they make mistakes too.

Being a parent is a difficult role. Trying to strike the balance between being a 'good' parent and a 'bad' one, is difficult. Many parents find it very difficult to acknowledge that their children are growing up and making choices without them. They know in their hearts that you have to live and learn by the choices you make, but this won't stop them from trying to protect you every step of the way.

If you find you are having real trouble with your parents then at least try and talk to them. Tell them why you're doing what you're doing and why they are upsetting you. This can be hard when you're both talking in defence, so whatever you do, don't get angry.

If you have parents that have problems then that's a different kettle of fish altogether. Perhaps they argue constantly and you live in fear that they are going to get divorced or separate. If this is the case it's important to remember, that just because your parents no longer love each other, it doesn't mean they no longer love you. People fall in and out of love all the time and many find it's easier on everyone if they end their relationship rather than go through forty years of constant fighting.

If your parents have severe problems with alcohol, drugs or are violent towards you in any way whatsoever, then you need to seek help. Sometimes, no amount of talking can help and the only way to protect yourself is to seek outside help. This means telling another adult you trust, perhaps, a friend's parents, a relative or a teacher. If you cannot face doing this then contact any one of the helplines at the back of the book and they will help you.

Sometimes, parents aren't the problem but brothers and sisters are. Each week on *Just 17*, I receive hundreds of letters from people who claim to either hate their brothers/sisters or are jealous/annoyed with them in some way. I can tell you from my experience that I grew up always in two minds about my brothers. I either absolutely loathed them or adored them. There never seemed to be an in-between. I cringe now when I think of the times we screamed at each other so loud that the neighbours complained to my poor long suffering mother. These days we all laugh about those times and agree that no matter what happened we could never live with each other ever again. But this doesn't stop us from all getting on wonderfully now. The real trick here is to try and treat your siblings the way you treat your friends. When I think back I would never have treated any friend of mine the way I treated my brothers and vice versa. But then sometimes, that's what being a family is all about.

So, the next time, you feel like life is never-ending and your family is driving you mad, bear in mind it won't be like this forever. And one day, when you've moved out and you're living by yourself, you'll look back to the days when the house was always crowded, people were always arguing and you always had company, with a certain fondness.

# HOW DOES *your* *place in the* FAMILY *affect your* personality?

Recent surveys show that your place in your family affects more than where you sit at the dinner table. It can actually affect your life in quite a mind-blowing way.

43

# 1 You really want to watch *Pretty Woman* on Video but the rest of the family want to watch the TV. What do you do?

- [ ] **a** Throw a tantrum and say, 'Right well, I'll just go and sit in my room all alone then'.
- [ ] **b** Have a jolly good moan but then sit and watch TV with them.
- [ ] **c** Agree to watch it after they've watched TV.

# 2 If there's a big family argument going on, what are you likely to be doing?

- [ ] **a** Trying to stop everyone from shouting and make the peace.
- [ ] **b** Arguing ferociously for your rights.
- [ ] **c** Tearfully saying, 'It's not fair, everyone picks on me'.

# 3 Which adjectives best describe your personality?

- [ ] **a** Charming and funny.
- [ ] **b** Communicative and individual.
- [ ] **c** Trustworthy and strong.

# 4 Your mother goes out for the day and leaves a whole list of jobs round the house to be done. Are you more likely to . . .

- [ ] **a** Do them as soon and as quickly as possible so you can go out with your friends.
- [ ] **b** Do them as well as you can, taking care to make sure

they are done properly.

- [ ] **C** Go out with your friends and say you forgot to do them.

## 5 What's your most popular refrain around the house?

- [ ] **a** No-one tells me anything.
- [ ] **b** It's not fair.
- [ ] **C** Do this!

## 6 When it comes to friends, do you

- [ ] **a** Have lots of friends and are always on the phone to them.
- [ ] **b** Have one or two close ones, but prefer your boyfriend.
- [ ] **C** Have lots of friends and boyfriends.

## 7 Do you know what you want to do when you leave school?

- [ ] **a** Yes, you intend to get a high-powered job with lots of money and prestige.
- [ ] **b** No, not yet. You're really not sure what direction you want to go in.
- [ ] **C** You don't want a conventional career like everyone else. You intend to do something completely different.

## 8 How do your parents describe you?

- [ ] **a** Headstrong and fickle.

b Sweet but difficult.

c A hard worker.

## 9 Do you often wish you could change your family and have . . .

a More brothers and sisters.

b No brothers and sisters.

c You don't want to change things. You're happy with the way things are.

## 10 Do your parents argue with you more because you're . . .

a Too bossy and stubborn.

b Too argumentative and stroppy.

c Too spoilt and rude.

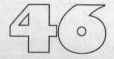

1  a 10      b 5       c 0

2  a 5       b 10      c 0

3  a 0       b 5       c 10

4  a 5       b 10      c 0

5  a 0       b 5       c 10

6  a 5       b 0       c 10

7  a 10      b 0       c 5

8  a 5       b 0       c 10

9  a 5       b 0       c 10

10 a 10      b 5       c 0

scores

47

### 0 – 30 THE BABY OR THE ONLY CHILD

The chances are you are either the youngest in your family or an only child. You've lead a pretty charmed existence and are at your best in the spotlight. Love and attention have been lavished on you because you either have older brothers and sisters to protect you and/or parents who have more time for you. You've learnt the value of being cute and charming but you feel pretty hard done by and picked on. Hence your rebellious and moody nature. Be careful, surveys show that the youngest or only child can often become the resident clown or a waster when they find the real world isn't like their home world.

### 35 – 65 THE MIDDLE OR IN BETWEEN CHILD

If you're a middle or in between child you're probably very well adjusted and a good communicator. You're used to being in the middle of arguments and more often than not you become the peace maker. You like being an outsider looking in, but you often feel taken for granted and trodden upon. This is why you are anxious to establish your individuality and look for ways to stand out from the crowd. There's no way you're going to get lost amongst a group because you know how to yell the loudest thanks to that bossy older sibling and that attention-grabbing younger one.

### 70 – 100 THE ELDEST CHILD

Being the firstborn, everything you have ever done has probably been scrutinised to death by your parents. Elder children are likely to become high achievers and go-getters. But they are also inclined towards anxiety because of the pressure their parents put on them. Career-wise, you will be successful in any position where you are in control. At times, you wish everything didn't fall on your shoulders but you also quite like the recognition you receive for your drive and strength.

# *do you* TAKE yOUr FAMILY *for* granted?

Families: can't live with them, can't live without them! But how much do you take for granted when it comes to playing happy families?

**1** **Your mother spends all day cooking you a fabulous meal for your birthday. The trouble is you've forgotten to tell her you're going out. What would you do?**

☐ **a** Go out, after all you know she'll understand.
☐ **b** Break it to her gently and offer to stay for the meal then go out afterwards.
☐ **c** Put your friends on hold, after all you can see them tomorrow.

**2** **You haven't got anything planned for the weekend. Then you find out your parents are going out. How do you feel?**

☐ **a** Annoyed because now you're going to be on your own.
☐ **b** A bit peeved because you're bored.
☐ **c** Happy because you've got the whole house to yourself.

**3** **Your mum wants you to take your younger sister to the cinema with your friends. What do you say?**

☐ **a** No way. You're not having her cramp your style.
☐ **b** Sure why not, you never know when you might need to go out with her friends.
☐ **c** Agree but moan about it all night.

**4** **You find out that your parents aren't taking you on holiday this year because they want to**

spend the money on the house instead. How do you feel?

☐ **a** Quite happy. It gives you lots of time to see all your friends.

☐ **b** A bit peeved because now you won't have a suntan to show off.

☐ **c** Really annoyed, what are you going to do all summer?

## 5 If there is a family argument going on where are you likely to be?

☐ **a** Right in the midst of it.

☐ **b** Upstairs in your bedroom.

☐ **c** It depends if it's anything to do with you or not.

## 6 You're out with your friends and you suddenly realise you're going to be an hour late getting home. What do you do?

☐ **a** Call your parents – you don't want them to worry.

☐ **b** Try and get home as quickly as possible.

☐ **c** Shrug, you're late already so why rush?

## 7 Your parents go away for the weekend and leave the house to you. Would you have a party?

☐ **a** Yes.

☐ **b** Yes, but only a small one with a few friends.

☐ **c** No, you couldn't bear the hassle.

## 8 What word best describes how your parents think of you?

- **a** Sensible
- **b** Careless
- **c** Irresponsible

## 9 What's your idea of a wonderful Christmas?

- **a** Being surrounded by family and having a huge home – cooked meal.
- **b** Lots of presents and food.
- **c** Falling in love with a handsome ski instructor in the Alps.

## 10 Your parents hate your boyfriend and want you to dump him. What would you do?

- **a** Ignore them. After all, what do they know?
- **b** Try to reason with them but still see him behind their backs.
- **c** Agree. After all they must have a pretty good reason.

52

**1**   a 0     b 5     c 10

**2**   a 0     b 5     c 10

**3**   a 0     b 10     c 5

**4**   a 10     b 5     c 0

**5**   a 0     b 10     c 5

**6**   a 10     b 5     c 0

**7**   a 0     b 5     c10

**8**   a 10     b 5     c 0

**9**   a 10     b 5     c 10

**10**   a 0     b 5     c 10

scores

53

### 0 – 35

**H**ow do your family put up with your behaviour? One of these days you're going to realise that the world doesn't owe you a living and this is going to give you a pretty big shock. Not everyone's going to let you take them for granted. Lighten up a bit and stop giving everyone a hard time. If your family annoys you then calmly tell them why. Don't let things build up to the point of explosion and then stamp your feet. Sure, you need your privacy and peace but so do they!

### 40 – 75

**W**ell, you've got the balance just right. You love your family and try not to take them for granted but you also know you can't be perfect all the time. Just as long as you keep apologising when you're wrong and still fight for what you believe in when you think they're wrong, you'll have no worries.

### 80 – 100

**W**ell, you're either one of The Brady Bunch or maybe you've told a few teeny weeny lies. But to give you the benefit of the doubt, I'll just say that you are a parent's dream. You say, do and know all the right things to make your family stay calm and happy. There's no way anyone could ever accuse you of taking anyone for granted. Good on you.

# HEALTH and looks

# HEALTH and *looks*

Take a look at yourself in the mirror. What do you see? A body you're happy with, or a body you hate? If you're like 98% of the female population, you probably loathe quite a lot of your body and what's more would do anything in the world to look like one of the supermodels.

56

*A* recent survey showed that 60% of people in the UK are on some kind of diet but the same survey shows that only a third of these actually need to lose any weight at all. Most people are unhappy with the way they look because they have low self-esteem and a poor self-image.

It's easy to look through magazines and see beautiful thin models with perfect skin and healthy hair. But the reality is these models have imperfections too. A friend of mine is a model and she grew up hating the fact that she was, in her words, 'a string bean'. To her the magazines all showed curvy girls with cleavages and stunning looks and she spent many years looking in the mirror wishing her looks away. Nowadays she still gets spots, lumps in the wrong places and bad hair. But these days she has a team of make-up artists, hairdressers and professional photographers whose job it is to make sure she looks perfect for the magazines. She often has to spend three hours getting ready for one shot. If someone spent that long getting you ready for a picture you'd look beautiful too.

Remember, even the most desired and beautiful people in the world despised their own looks at some point in their lives. Just a few examples are Marilyn Monroe, Madonna, Cindy Crawford and supermodel Kate Moss. The simple fact is, at the end of the day beauty really is only skin deep. It matters more what's going on in your mind and what you do with your life. As the old adage goes, 'when your soul's at ease so is your body'.

Learning to love the whole of your body, even the bits you really loathe, is an important part of growing up. Sometimes, we'll become convinced that if only we were thinner, fatter, had more of a bust or were taller, things would be better. But life only gets better when you make a decision to look on the positive side. Do you really believe being a size 10 will make men fall at your feet, help you to pass your exams and make you become Miss Popularity? I doubt it very much and what's more you can have all these things no matter what you look like. Take a few famous people as an example: Dawn French, Ruby Wax, Roseanne Barr, Madonna, Julia Roberts, Susan Sarandon. None of them have classic model looks and yet all of them are successful in their own right.

Of course, beauty does make an impression but a smile, being friendly and thoughtful has a far more long lasting effect on a person. I doubt very much that you're the sort of person who judges someone by how much they weigh or how tall they are (if you are, then you're never going to make long-lasting friends) and if you don't do it, then why would anyone else judge you this way?

Dissatisfaction with our looks isn't limited to weight. Some of us are unhappy about particular features, perhaps a nose, or ears or skin. Often, something which looks huge, ugly and revolting to us is, in fact, unnoticeable to others. For example, the other night I was out with some friends when one of them kept commenting about this huge spot she had on her chin. At first none of us could even see it but by the end of the night we were all rivetted by it. This just goes to show, it's only by constantly drawing attention to something we don't like that it becomes a visible problem.

If, on the other hand, you're so unhappy about a part of your body that it's affecting your life to the point where you no longer want to go out, then it's time to do something. A visit to your doctor can sort out everything from skin problems to nose/ear and diet worries. Getting a medical opinion has done wonders for many people and if you are in the 1% who actually has a serious grievance about your features then your doctor can help you to see a specialist who can help further.

If you have low self-esteem and a bad self-image, you can do a number of things to help yourself. Start by looking in the mirror. Instead of looking at yourself with disgust and hate, try focusing on your good points (and we all have them). Tell yourself that it doesn't matter that you have fat thighs/a small bust/ lumps and bumps in strange places, because they are all part of you. Remember, if you don't like yourself how can you expect anyone else to like you. People are always attracted to people who are happy and positive about themselves. So instead of sitting about feeling that the world is dreadful because you don't look perfect, concentrate on being the happiest you can with what you've got. After all, no matter what you believe, beauty really is in the eye of the beholder.

# ARE YOU A vain VANESSA *or a modest mandy?*

Let's face it at the end of the day we're all pretty vain aren't we? Who hasn't walked past a shop window and gazed at their reflection? But are you someone who takes their looks too far or can't even bear to look in the mirror?

## 1 When you walk past a shop window and see your reflection, what do you do?

☐ **a** Gaze at yourself for at least 10 hours. You never realised how beautiful you really were.

☐ **b** Take a quick look, rush to the nearest litter bin and throw up.

☐ **c** Pretend you're looking at the clothes in the window, but secretly have a jolly good look at yourself.

## 2 You're standing in front of your bedroom mirror and for a laugh say 'Mirror, mirror, on the wall who is the fairest of them all?' You're shocked to hear it reply, but what does it say?

☐ **a** Nothing, it just smashes.

☐ **b** Well, you're okay but I prefer ( and proceeds to reel off a list of names).

☐ **c** YOU, YOU, YOU!

## 3 You pass two boys chatting on a bus and one says, 'Isn't she lovely?' Who do you think they're talking about?

☐ **a** It could be the girl next to you, then again it could be you.

☐ **b** The conductor, the woman with the baby, the girl next to you, anyone, in fact but you.

☐ **c** You of course, who else?

61

## 4 You hear your boyfriend describe you as being 'interesting'. What's your reaction?

- [ ] **a** You're flattered. He knows there's more to life than a pretty face.
- [ ] **b** Agony. It means you're ugly.
- [ ] **c** Annoyance. You're beautiful and that's the most interesting thing about you.

## 5 Your new boyfriend is painfully untrendy and uncool. Would you introduce him to your friends?

- [ ] **a** Yes, but give him a makeover first.
- [ ] **b** No way. He's all right by himself but heaven forbid anyone you know should meet him.
- [ ] **c** Not even the uncool boys would ask you out!

## 6 Who do people say is the pretty one out of you and your best friend?

- [ ] **a** You, of course, and you make sure she knows it.
- [ ] **b** Your best friend because she's so nice.
- [ ] **c** You've never really thought about it.

## 7 Someone comments that you and your mother look like sisters. What's your reaction?

- [ ] **a** You scream and faint at the idea. You can't look that old!
- [ ] **b** Feel pleased for your mum.
- [ ] **c** Feel jealous because you think your mum looks better than you.

## 8 Which famous person would you most like to be compared to?

- [ ] **a** Cindy Crawford
- [ ] **b** Er. . .You couldn't possibly look like anyone famous even if you tried.
- [ ] **c** You don't care, but someone who is more than a pretty face.

## 9 All the magazines are saying flares are the thing to wear. You know they don't suit you but what do you do?

- [ ] **a** Stay in till the fashion changes.
- [ ] **b** Laugh at all the people wearing them. After all you were wearing them last year before they hit the high street stores.
- [ ] **c** Nothing. You wear what suits you, you don't follow fashion.

## 10 You say to your best friend, 'God I look a real state today' – what does she say?

- [ ] **a** Don't be silly. You look fabulous as ever.
- [ ] **b** You'd never say that because you never look a state.
- [ ] **c** Mmm . . . you could try a bit harder with your hair/clothes/make up etc . . .

# Scores

**1** a 10    b 5    c 0

**2** a 0    b 5    c 10

**3** a 5    b 0    c 10

**4** a 5    b 0    c 10

**5** a 5    b 10    c 0

**6** a 10    b 0    c 5

**7** a 10    b 5    c 0

**8** a 10    b 0    c 5

**9** a 0    b 10    c 5

**10** a 5    b 10    c 0

### 0 – 40 MODEST MANDY

Well, you're certainly not vain are you? In fact, you don't have to worry about people putting you down because no-one could quite match the terrible things you say about yourself. You have a very low self-image and your esteem seems to be a rock bottom. It's time to start being nicer to yourself and your body. So what if you're not perfect, no-one is. Start listening to your friends and the next time someone gives you a compliment, don't throw it away. Accept it gracefully and believe what they say. You've spent so long believing all the slights that come your way, you've forgotten what a lovely person you really are. So take another peek in the mirror and give yourself a chance.

### 45 – 75 SUSSED SALLY

Well done, you've got the balance right. You know there is more to the world than having a pretty face and good legs. Intelligence, thoughtfulness and a smile go a lot further in your opinion and how right you are. You've got a good head on your shoulders and no doubt you are a well sought after person to be around. Keep up the good work.

### 80 –100 VAIN VANESSA

If you could just pull yourself away from that mirror for a moment, there might be a few interesting things here for you to note. A pretty face isn't all that matters in this world. If you just spend your days concentrating on your looks and your clothes, you're soon going to find yourself friendless and/or surrounded by equally shallow people. You should never judge a book by it's cover and the sooner you realise this the better. It's about time you and your reflection got together and realised it's time to put a bit of substance into your life.

# HAVE YOU *got an* image *problem?*

Do you worry constantly that you don't look good enough? Are you afraid that you'll never get a boyfriend? Are mirrors your idea of a nightmare? If so you may have an image problem.

## 1 What does the sight of a weight machine do to you?

- [ ] **a** Have you running in the opposite direction.
- [ ] **b** Not much, you have one at home and you weigh yourself every day.
- [ ] **c** Nothing, you don't care about weighing yourself. You know what feels right and what doesn't.

## 2 You're in Top Shop and you want to try on a dress but they only have communal changing-rooms. What do you do?

- [ ] **a** Go ahead and try it on.
- [ ] **b** Risk buying it without trying it on.
- [ ] **c** Fling it back at the assistant and storm out in a huff.

## 3 What season do you prefer?

- [ ] **a** Summer because you can strip off to the bare essentials.
- [ ] **b** Winter because you can cover yourself up totally.
- [ ] **c** Spring because you can wear whatever you like.

## 4 Your boyfriend comments that you've put on weight. What do you do?

- [ ] **a** Scream at him like a banshee and then go on a strict diet.

**b** Say, so what?

**c** Agree but comment that you prefer looking this way.

# 5 Your best friend buys a dress that looks fabulous on her. How do you feel?

**a** Happy for her but slightly envious.

**b** Jealous and fed up. You'll never look that good.

**c** She's fabulous anyway no matter what she wears.

# 6 Do you constantly ask for reassurance from your family/friends/boyfriend, on how you look?

**a** No.

**b** Yes.

**c** It depends on your mood.

# 7 How many of the clothes in your wardrobe do you wear?

**a** All of them.

**b** Hardly any of them. You stick to one or two items only.

**c** Most of them.

# 8 You walk past a mirror in a shop. Do you have a look at what you look like?

**a** No, because you don't want to ruin your day.

**b** Yes, you're curious to see if your hair is sticking up.

**c** Of course, you'd be lying if you said no.

# 9 You walk past a group of boys. One of them says, 'What a pretty girl'. What do you do?

**a** Turn round to see who they're talking about.

**b** Smile and say, 'Thank you'.

**c** Ignore them but feel secretly pleased.

# 10 Are you the sort of person who gives and takes compliments?

**a** Yes, you like to tell people they're looking nice.

**b** No, you never give them and no-one gives you serious ones back.

**c** Yes, only if you're looking good too.

**1**    a 0      b 5      c 10

**2**    a 10      b 5      c 0

**3**    a 10      b 0      c 5

**4**    a 0      b 10      c 5

**5**    a 5      b 0      c 10

**6**    a 10      b 0      c 5

**7**    a 10      b 0      c 5

**8**    a 0      b 10      c 5

**9**    a 0      b 10      c 5

**10**   a 10      b 0      c 5

## 0 – 35

You have a bit of a serious problem with your self-image. You try to hide yourself as much as possible because you don't really like your body an awful lot. This stops you from doing things you want. Instead of hiding yourself away, try taking a more honest look at yourself. You're not as hideous as you think. In fact, we'll bet you're just fine.

## 40 – 75

You have good days and bad days. On your good days you feel your body will do just fine. You'll wear what you want, go dancing in that skimpy, black dress and chat up anyone you want, and good for you. But on bad days, forget it. If this is the case, then it's time to start realising that your body doesn't change that much, it's all to do with your attitude. Try thinking more positively about your body, and your bad days will get less and less.

## 80 – 100

Lucky you, you don't have a self image problem at all. You've learnt that you're far happier being content with what you've got. So what if you're never going to look like Kate Moss? You know the secret to happiness, after all, if there was only one type of beauty, the world would be an awfully boring place.

# BOYS & love

Most of the letters I receive on *Just 17* are from girls worried about boys and love. Boys, to a lot of girls, are these strange species who are impossible to understand. They act strangely, do weird things and you can never pin them down.

73

Mind you, the letters I receive from boys say just the same thing about us girls. I think the important key to understanding boys is that we are all essentially the same.

None of us are born with the ability to be wonderful boyfriends and girlfriends. It's something we have to learn like everything else. Boys don't have a special quality that makes them able to ask girls out and likewise they don't come equipped to understand how our minds work.

No-one really knows what love is or how to tell when you're in love. All I can tell you is that love is complicated. It means a hundred different things to a hundred different people. Sometimes, it makes you feel as if you're on top of the world while at other times you feel like you're plummeting into a dark, dark hole.

There is no guarantee to having a wonderful relationship, all I can say is that the basis of love should always be trust. If you haven't got that then you haven't got anything. Treat your boyfriend the way you expect him to treat you. Don't play games with him, like flirting to make him jealous or pretending to be angry when you're not. These are sure ways to lose him. Taking him for granted and letting him down at the last minute is also a route to disaster.

If you want to get someone's attention then start by smiling in their direction and saying hello when you meet. It's important to try and talk to them, otherwise how are you ever going to know whether you like them or not. Also, don't wait for them to ask you out, why don't you do it. There's no rule saying boys have to do the asking. Don't make a big deal of it just be casual and take it slowly.

Some girls go absolutely boy crazy and become so dependent on their boyfriend that they forget about all their friends and family. Try to stop yourself from doing this because if your relationship ends you'll have no-one around to pick you up and dust you down. Also how would you like to have someone stuck to your side 24 hours a day. Remember you were separate people before you started dating and you still are.

Once you're in a relationship, make sure you talk whenever something's bothering you. The amount of relationships that hit the dust because no-one says what they think is amazing. But if your boyfriend is treating you badly, abusing you in any way or making you more miserable than happy, then it's time to move on without him.

If you find your relationship crumbling and your dreams of love falling apart, don't despair. Falling out of love can be one of the hardest things you'll ever have to bear, but the pain does get better. Just when you think you are going to sit in that chair for the rest of your life and stare at that wall forever, life will brighten up.

Some days will be wonderful and some will be bad. Whatever you do, don't put yourself down. Remember, you are still that wonderful person he fell for all those months ago.

Call your friends up, moan about him, mull over your relationship, then go out and make yourself busy. This means making yourself do things instead of moping about. You may not want another boyfriend now, but in time you will, and getting into the habit of sitting about on your own won't help when you feel ready for this.

Whatever your status may be right now on the love front, hopefully these three quizzes on love, boys and relationships will help you to find out just what you want from boys.

75

# LOVE
## *can you*
# handle
## ♥ *it?*

Love is wonderful, love hurts, love is everything and nothing. The question is, can you
handle it? Can you deal with those awkward
moments, those love-splattered times, or are
you destined to always make a hash of it?

76

♥ ♥ ♥ ♥ ♥ ♥ ♥ ♥ ♥ ♥ ♥ ♥

**1** You've got a boyfriend but secretly fancy another boy. What do you do?

☐ **a** Stick with your present boyfriend till you have a chance to catch this new boy.

☐ **b** Nothing, you can't bear to hurt your present boyfriend.

☑ **c** Break up with your boyfriend. What's the point of dating him when you like someone else.

**2** How can you tell when a boy is in love with you?

☐ **a** He lavishes you with expensive presents.

☑ **b** He calls you now and again.

☑ **c** He'll be there for you no matter what time of day it is.

**3** If you want to get your boyfriend's attention at a party what do you do?

☐ **a** Flirt outrageously with his friends, laugh loudly and dance wildly with every boy in the room.

☑ **b** Go up to him and chat away.

☐ **c** Sulk like mad and throw a strop.

**4** Your boyfriend informs you he is off on holiday with his mates for two weeks. What do you do?

☐ **a** Say, 'What a good idea' and arrange to go away with your mates.

☐ **b** Cry and cry – it's obviously a sign he doesn't want to be with you.

☐ **c** Spend the two weeks wracked with jealousy because you're imagining all those European girls after his body.

## 5 You're off to the video shop with the man of your dreams. He's picking the film. What is it likely to be?

☐ **a** *Revenge of The Killer Zombies.*
☑ **b** *Ghost.*
☐ **c** *Home Alone.*

## 6 When you're both together, out with your friends, how do you behave?

☐ **a** You kiss and snog all night; at dinner, at a club, at the cinema, and ignore everyone else.
☐ **b** You just have a laugh with all your friends, after all, you're not joined at the hip.
☑ **c** You always sit together but make sure you talk to other people.

## 7 The boy you thought you were in love with breaks up with you. What do you do?

☐ **a** Retire to your room, with a box of Kleenex, your best friends and cry for a week.
☐ **b** Refuse to shed a tear and do your best to get your own back on him.
☐ **c** Go out with one of his friends.

## 8 What famous couple do you imagine you and your boyfriend to be?

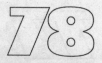

☐ **a** Romeo and Juliet.
☐ **b** Demi Moore and Bruce Willis.
☐ **c** Julia Roberts and Lyle Lovett.

## 9 Your boyfriend tells you his ex has rung up and wants to see him. What do you say?

☐ **a** 'Not if you ever want to see me again'.
☐ **b** 'Why not? As long as I can come along'.
☑ **c** 'Okay, after all I'm friends with my ex'.

## 10 You have a massive fight and it's all your fault. Two days later you still haven't seen him. What do you do?

☑ **a** Call him up, apologise and promise never to do it again.
☐ **b** Get your friend to tell him you're sorry and hope for the best.
☐ **c** Wait for him to come round.

**1** a 0  b 5  c 10

**2** a 5  b 0  c 10

**3** a 0  b 10  c 5

**4** a 10  b 0  c 5

**5** a 0  b 10  c 5

**6** a 0  b 10  c 5

**7** a 10  b 5  c 0

**8** a 5  b 10  c 0

**9** a 0  b 5  c 10

**10** a 10  b 5  c 10

80

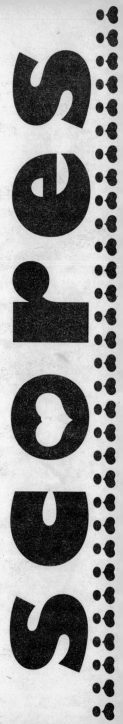

## 0 – 30

Mmm … you're not too good at handling love are you? Forget all those slushy films you've been watching, real love just isn't like that. Smothering your boyfriend and behaving like a human limpet will have him running for the door in two minutes. Love may be all roses and kisses but it's also about space and trust. Lighten up a bit, let your boyfriend do his own thing once in a while, and you do yours. You'll be surprised how great it will be for your relationship.

## 35 – 70

Well, you've nearly got it. You know just how to behave on the outside when it comes to love but internally you're all churned up. Try not to worry so much. It's okay to feel jealous, scared and insecure, love is all these things too. Just make sure you don't bottle these anxieties up. Talk to your boyfriend, let him know how you feel and let him put your mind at rest and then you'll feel on top of the world.

## 75 – 100

Well, I'm jealous. You've pretty much got things sussed and what's more you've got a man to match. You know that love can be soppy and cute but it also has to be practical and workable and that's just what you've got. You both give each other space to do what you want and at the same time know just when it's time to come together again. Good on you both!

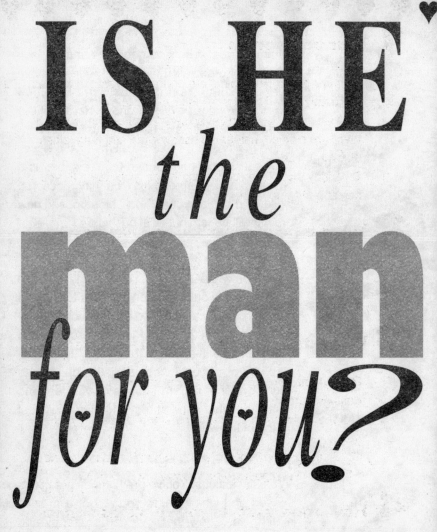

# IS HE *the* man *for you?*

**Great minds think alike or fools never differ? Which one do you believe in when it comes to finding your ideal partner? Try this quiz and find out what type of man you want.** ♥

## 1 Your bedroom is :

- [ ] **a** Immaculate. The books are on the shelves, the clothes are neatly folded and there's no rubbish in sight.
- [ ] **b** Disgusting. You can't even see the carpet because there are clothes, half-eaten sandwiches and magazines all over the floor.
- [ ] **C** Untidy, but clean. You leave things lying about till you can't bear it any longer.

## 2 What type of music do you like best?

- [ ] **a** Rock, of course, lots of loud guitars and long hair.
- [ ] **b** Anything that's in the chart that you can dance to.
- [ ] **C** Anything alternative, none of this manufactured rubbish.

## 3 What do you do in your spare time?

- [ ] **a** Anything sporty. You like going out into the fresh air and getting exercise.
- [ ] **b** Watch videos, go to the cinema and shop with your mates.
- [ ] **C** Sit in your bedroom listening to music and imagining what your life is going to be like when you're older.

## 4 How important do you think fashion is?

- [ ] **a** Not very. You couldn't care less what people wear as long as they are comfortable.
- [ ] **b** Fairly important. You like people to look smart.
- [ ] **C** Very important. You like to wear the latest fashions.

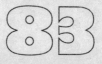

# 5 You've won a holiday anywhere in the world. Where would you go?

- [ ] **a** Australia because it's so far away and you know you'd have an adventure there.
- [ ] **b** Los Angeles because it's glamorous and full of stars.
- [ ] **c** Euro-Disney because it's not too far and you love amusement parks.

# 6 What's your idea of a perfect date?

- [ ] **a** A candlelit dinner for two somewhere remote and romantic.
- [ ] **b** A concert and then on to a club with all your mates.
- [ ] **c** A party where you can be with him all night and still see your friends.

# 7 Your ideal home is?

- [ ] **a** A huge flat in the centre of a city with all the latest hi-tech stuff.
- [ ] **b** A country house, miles from anywhere with loads of animals.
- [ ] **c** A house in the suburbs with a garage and a lovely garden.

# 8 What's likely to put you right off someone?

- [ ] **a** Rudeness, you can't bear it.
- [ ] **b** Someone who burps and lets off wind in public.
- [ ] **c** Someone who is stingy with their money.

**9** Three guys ask you out at the same time. You like them all but who is likely to win your heart?

- ☐ **a** The one who makes you laugh the most.
- ☐ **b** The one who gives you the most compliments.
- ☐ **c** The one who ignores you.

**10** What kind of job would you like your ideal man to have?

- ☐ **a** Anything that makes him happy.
- ☐ **b** A musician or actor.
- ☐ **c** Something in the caring professions.

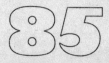

**1** a 10     b 0     c 5

**2** a 0     b 10     c 5

**3** a 10     b 5     c 0

**4** a 0     b 10     c 5

**5** a 10     b 5     c 0

**6** a 10     b 0     c 5

**7** a 0     b 10     c 5

**8** a 0     b 10     c 5

**9** a 5     b 10     c 0

**10** a 0     b 5     c 10

Scores

## 0 – 25 Mr Cool & Laid Back

You're pretty casual about life aren't you? Nothing bothers you much. You can't be doing with all that unnecessary worrying about fashion, or all that jumping about that exercise involves. Your ideal man is someone who is cool about life. Someone who doesn't care what you wear, whether your hair is greasy and how much money you've got. In fact, as long as he's happy you couldn't care less what he looks like or what he does for a living, as long as he's a nice person. If you want to catch him, hang out at a museum or down at the resident art cafe.

## 30 – 65 Mr Glam

You are so hip it hurts. You wear the right clothes, like the right music and hang out with the right people. Your ideal man is someone who is just as image conscious as you. Someone who's not too sporty, you can't be doing with all that sweatiness and muscle, and who's into going out. Try for someone in the media, a musician or an actor. No doubt you admire lots of famous people and have set your sights on being the next Hollywood Couple. To get this man, hang out at the hippest club in town and/or your local drama centre.

## 70 – 100 Mr Sporty & Intelligent

Sportiness and intelligence, that's what you're after. Forget all those Hollywood couples or those laid back types, you intend to land someone reliable and respect-worthy. You see yourself as part of a winning team, you've got big ambitions and want someone to share them with you. If you want to land your man, hang about on those sport fields, or down at your local university, better still, concentrate on becoming mega intelligent and they'll land in your lap.

# IS THIS a relationship made in HEAVEN or in HELL?

So, you've landed the man of your dreams, you think this is it, but just how likely is your relationship to succeed? Try this quiz and find out.

88

♥ ♥ ♥ ♥ ♥ ♥ ♥ ♥ ♥ ♥ ♥ ♥ ♥

# 1 You want to stay in but your boyfriend wants to go to a party. What do you do?

☐ **a** Argue about it then cry your eyes out when he goes out and leaves you alone.

☐ **b** Compromise, spend an hour at the party with him then both come home.

☐ **c** You stay in and your boyfriend goes out. He's free to do whatever he wants.

# 2 You hate the way your boyfriend dresses. He makes Grunge rockers look positively smart. What do you do?

☐ **a** Drop some subtle hints when you go shopping and then buy him some clothes.

☐ **b** Not much. It's up to him how he dresses.

☐ **c** Refuse to go out with him unless he smartens up his act.

# 3 You hear a rumour that your boyfriend has two-timed you, what do you do?

☐ **a** Ask his best friend out.

☐ **b** Call him up and explain what you've heard and see what he says.

☐ **c** Forget about it, until someone mentions it again.

# 4 You really want to see the new Demi Moore weepie but your boyfriend doesn't want to go. What would he do in the end?

☐ **a** Go but moan all the way through it.
☐ **b** Call up one of his friends and pay them to go with you.
☐ **c** Watch TV while you moan and then go out with his friends.

# 5 How often does your boyfriend mention his ex-girlfriend?

☐ **a** Only when the topic comes up.
☐ **b** All the time. He never stops comparing you to her.
☐ **c** Now and again, just to get a reaction out of you.

# 6 What is more likely to upset him?

☐ **a** Arsenal winning the league.
☐ **b** You in a skimpy leather number.
☐ **c** An argument about loyalty.

# 7 You're out at a restaurant when your boyfriend starts having a row with your best friend. What do you do?

☐ **a** Ignore them. It's their argument not yours.
☐ **b** See who's in the right and take their side.
☐ **c** Take your best friend's side.

# 8 Your parents hate him for no reason and forbid you to see him again. What would you do?

☐ **a** Still see him behind their backs. After all it's your life.
☐ **b** Chuck him.
☐ **c** Still see him but let him know how much they dislike him.

## 9 You're at a party, how does your boyfriend behave?

 **a** He gets wildly drunk with his mates and then makes a total fool of himself.

**b** Like he normally does, but he makes sure he smooches with you when the slow songs come on.

**c** He ignores you all night and flirts like crazy.

## 10 What's the nicest thing your boyfriend has ever said to you?

**a** I love you.

**b** Make us a cup of tea, love.

**c** You look nice.

**1** a 0         b 10         c 5

**2** a 10         b 5         c 0

**3** a 0         b 10         c 5

**4** a 10         b 5         c 0

**5** a 10         b 0         c 5

**6** a 0         b 5         c 10

**7** a 5         b 10         c 0

**8** a 10         b 0         c 5

**9** a 5         b 10         c 0

**10** a 10         b 0         c 5

scores

### 0 – 30

This is a match made in hell and don't you just know it! Just why are you going out with this man? He shows you no consideration, affection or loyalty. But let's give him the benefit of the doubt for a moment and say he doesn't realise what a thick-skinned fool he's being. If this is the case then tell him to shape up or else. You deserve better and if you get rid of him, you'll find it.

### 35 – 65

Your match is somewhere between heaven and hell. It's nearly there but not quite. He annoys you at times and vice versa. Instead of being indifferent to his annoying habits, point them out now and again. Tell him why he's upset you. He's not a mind reader and he'll never change if you don't tell him what's wrong. This relationship has the potential to be marvellous so give it a go.

### 70 – 100

This is a love made in heaven. You're so compatible and no doubt everyone holds you up as the ideal couple. You both know the answer to most problems is compromise. In an argument it doesn't matter who is right and who is wrong as long as you both agree in the end. Well done, your relationship is bound to go from strength to strength.

# school

# & how to survive it

# school

## & how to ★ ★ ★ survive *it*

Despite what some people may say, school days are rarely the best days your life. However, they are a big chunk of your life and this means whether you like it or not, you have to go through with it. For most of us this means five days a week, till we're at least 16 years old. A long time, to sit around being miserable and fed up.

Going to school is rather like going to the dentist. You can avoid it and then pay for it later in life, or you can suffer it and find out that it really is for your own good and that the pain isn't that bad.

 95

★  ★  ★  ★  ★

*A* popular refrain is, "why do I have to learn all that useless stuff"? I felt very much this way when I was at school but now I can honestly say most of the lessons have helped me in some way. For instance, all that boring map reading in Geography has helped me while I'm driving. English lessons gave me an appreciation for reading, the cinema and art. Maths lessons have been invaluable when it comes to working out my finances, and even those dreadful Physics lessons have helped me in my house. So, you see whether you love it or hate it, school exposes you to more information than anything else you're ever likely to do in your life.

Of course, it stinks if you haven't got any friends or if a teacher is picking on you. Or if the lessons are too hard. Worse still, you may be being bullied and can't cope, but there are ways round all of these problems. If you feel lonely because you're new at school or don't know anyone,

why not try to get involved in some extracurricular activities. Most schools have computer clubs, drama classes, sports teams, the list is endless, all you have to do is make an effort.

If you have problems with a teacher and can't talk to him/her then ask for help. It's impossible to get on with everyone, I remember I had one German teacher who would pick on me for no reason. In the end I skived off his classes so much I failed the exams. Don't let that happen to you. If a teacher is picking on you, go and speak to another teacher, or ask to be transferred to a different class. Don't suffer just because they are being a bully.

And speaking of bullying, don't give in to it. Bullies often pick their victims for no reason whatsoever, so don't blame yourself for what's going on. They also rely on your silence to get away with their behaviour. The only way to solve it is to tell someone what's going on. Keep a note of what they do, and then this way you'll have evidence to back you up. Remember, bullies will ruin not only your day but your future, if you let them harass you out of school.

If your lessons are too hard and you can't cope with the work load, speak to your teachers and your parents. No-one expects you to know everything and cope with problems on your own. Believe it or not, the teachers at your school are there to help you and most of them do want the best for you.

At the end of the day a decent education is important so that you can get a good job, but this doesn't necessarily mean you have to get brilliant marks. Women like Anita Roddick of The Body Shop, and Debbie Moore of Pineapple Dance Studios fame weren't the class boffins and look where they are now. Doing the best that you can is all that you need to do.

97

# making
## *the*
# MOST
## *of*
# *school?*

★ ★ ★ ★ ★ ★ ★

**Does the mere mention of the word school strike fear in your heart and boredom in your soul? If so, perhaps, you're not giving your school a fair chance.**

**Try this quiz and see how you fare.**

★ ★ ★ ★ ★

# 1 You're ten minutes late for school and you know you're for it when you get there. What do you do?

- [ ] **a** Shrug it off, so what if you're late again, at least you're going.
- [ ] **b** Give up and go home, what's the point if you're late.
- [ ] **c** Run all the way there and sob for forgiveness when your form teacher starts yelling.

# 2 There are tryouts for all the school sports teams on Saturday morning. What do you do?

- [ ] **a** Sign up for them all, you'll get on one if it kills you.
- [ ] **b** Just go along for the netball one and hope for the best.
- [ ] **c** Sleep in till noon and then laugh at all the fools who got up early.

# 3 Your French teacher tells you the whole class are going on an exchange visit to Paris. What are your feelings about it?

- [ ] **a** You're overjoyed, it means a week of croissants, sexy French men and no school.
- [ ] **b** You're fairly pleased but worried about who you're going to end up with.
- [ ] **c** You're really happy, you've always wanted to see Paris and meet some real Parisians.

# 4 You have to choose between German and Geography lessons. How do you make

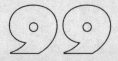

**the choice?**

- [ ] **a** See which class has the hunkiest teacher.
- [ ] **b** Decide which one will help you most in the future.
- [ ] **c** See which one finishes earlier.

## 5 You're snowed under with homework and can't cope. What are you likely to do?

- [ ] **a** Go completely wild, throw all your school books out of the window and declare your school days over.
- [ ] **b** Do the subjects you enjoy and forget about the rest.
- [ ] **c** Struggle through but ask your teachers for their help.

## 6 Where do you sit in lessons?

- [ ] **a** Anywhere where you can see the board clearly.
- [ ] **b** At the back of the class with all your mates, so the teachers can't see you chatting.
- [ ] **c** Next to your best friend behind someone large.

## 7 What kind of reputation do you have at school?

- [ ] **a** A wild one. You're the sort of girl always in detention, always in trouble and always skiving.
- [ ] **b** Your report card sums it up, 'Could try harder. She must learn to stop talking'.
- [ ] **c** The teachers have you pegged as a girl who will go far.

## 8 Are you planning to leave school:

- [ ] **a** As soon as your 16th birthday comes round.

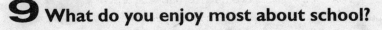

☐ **b** When you've got all your GCSEs.
☐ **c** Not till you get into university.

## 9 What do you enjoy most about school?

☐ **a** The bell that rings so you can go home at 3.30pm.
☐ **b** Seeing your friends.
☐ **c** A couple of lessons which you love.

## 10 How much of your lessons do you think is relevant?

☐ **a** Most of it. What isn't still gives you some insight
into life.
☐ **b** None of it. It's got absolutely nothing to do with real life.
☐ **c** One or two practical things help but the rest is rubbish.

# 1 a 5     b 0     c 10

# 2 a 10     b 5     c 0

# 3 a 0     b 5     c 10

# 4 a 0     b 10     c 5

# 5 a 0     b 5     c 10

# 6 a 10     b 0     c 5

# 7 a 0     b 5     c 10

# 8 a 0     b 5     c 10

# 9 a 0     b 5     c 10

# 10 a 10     b 0     c 5

scores

## results

### 0 – 30

Okay, so you hate school, but have you ever given it a fair chance? Is it really that boring and mundane? Surely there must be something that interests you. Believe me, compared to some jobs, school is absolute bliss. Think about changing your attitude, so what if you're not good at lessons, it doesn't mean you're a failure. Everyone has a talent and it doesn't have to be academic. So, don't be afraid to ask for help and/or to change classes if you don't like a particular subject. Trying sometimes, can make the world of difference.

### 35 – 70

I know exactly how you feel, school's okay but you'd rather it was all over now. You try just enough to get through your classes. You couldn't care less about being top of the class but you know better than to come bottom. You also excel at some lessons but fail in others. What you have to do is try to strike a more healthy balance. There's always going to be things in life you don't like doing but have to do, and school's good practice for this.

### 75 – 100

Congratulations, you may not love school but you're sure as hell going to get the most out of it. You know that school is the perfect opportunity to try your hand at anything you can and see how you fare. You know that you may never get a chance like this again, so you're not about to waste a moment of it. You'll go far.

# ARE YOU *COOLER than ice* OR **CREEPIER** *than a spider?*

School is about more than education, it's about learning to mix with other people, even the ones you don't like. How do you fare on the school like-ability scale?

104

★ ★ ★ ★ ★

# 1 A schoolfriend calls you up in tears at 8 o'clock on a Saturday night. If you talk to her you're going to miss getting to the cinema. What do you do?

☐ **a** Listen for five minutes then make your excuses and speak to her on Monday.

☐ **b** Put on a pretend voice and say you're not in.

☐ **c** Cancel your plans and rush round with a box of Kleenex.

# 2 In an English class, a new shy teacher asks you to stand up and read out a passage. What do you do?

☐ **a** Put on your silliest voice and make the class laugh.

☐ **b** Mumble and stutter in embarrassment till she asks you to sit down.

☐ **c** Refuse to do it on the grounds you need to rest your voice.

# 3 Your school is very strict about uniform. How well do you follow their rules?

☐ **a** Pretty well, if you consider orange flares and love beads a uniform.

☐ **b** You make sure your uniform is always neatly pressed and correctly worn.

☐ **c** You wear what you have to but try to adapt it as best you can.

# 4 You're busy cramming for a Chemistry

**test when an old ex-boyfriend calls round. What do you say?**

- ☐ **a** 'Sorry, can't chat, I'm off to a new club with my new boyfriend who's a musician!'
- ☐ **b** 'Sorry got to work, I'll call you sometime'.
- ☐ **c** Nothing. You slam the door in his face.

## 5 A teacher asks for volunteers to help her carry some books to her car. What do you do?

- ☐ **a** Jump up, take the books and even offer to carry her shopping for her.
- ☐ **b** Ignore her - you know someone else will do it.
- ☐ **c** Offer her a deal: one book for every 'A' grade she gives you.

## 6 You and your best friend have worked on a joint project together. In front of the class your teacher praises your friend not you. What do you do?

- ☐ **a** Feel betrayed by your friend and moan that she's teacher's pet to the rest of your class behind her back.
- ☐ **b** Jump up and announce your part in it.
- ☐ **c** Tell everyone she had nothing to do with it but the teacher felt sorry for her.

## 7 You're at the school disco, and it's full of attractive men. Who do you set your sights on?

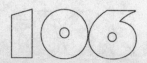

- [ ] **a** The DJ.
- [ ] **b** That cute boy in the fifth year you've been after for ages.
- [ ] **c** The hunky sports teacher.

## 8 What best describes your role at school?

- [ ] **a** The girl everyone tells their problems too and asks advice from.
- [ ] **b** The popular girl who can have any boy she wants, wears all the right clothes and all the teachers like her.
- [ ] **c** The academic one who gets great marks, is good at sport and will soon be Head Girl.

## 9 When a teacher asks a question in class, how likely are you to answer?

- [ ] **a** Very likely. You always make sure you know your stuff.
- [ ] **b** Not very. You're too busy chatting to notice the questions asked.
- [ ] **c** Never. You're no swot!

## 10 It's the last day of school. What do you do?

- [ ] **a** Go completely wild, tear off your uniform and rip it up in front of your teachers.
- [ ] **b** Cry because you're going to miss it so much.
- [ ] **c** Pack for your holiday.

**1** a 5    b 0    c 10

**2** a 10    b 5    c 0

**3** a 0    b 10    c 5

**4** a 0    b 5    c 10

**5** a 10    b 5    c 0

**6** a 5    b 10    c 0

**7** a 0    b 5    c 10

**8** a 5    b 0    c 10

**9** a 10    b 5    c 0

**10** a 0    b 10    c 5

### 0 – 30

Well, you're a real cool customer aren't you? Class joker and trend-setter, you're more worried about how you look and how many laughs you can get to bother about doing your homework or paying attention in class. It's great to be so cool but it isn't so cool to end up with no exams or a reputation that will never get you a good job reference. You can still be popular and do well at school. Concentrate on what you want in the future, not how you look to all your friends and teachers.

### 35 – 70

You've got the balance just right. You know when to be funny and when to listen. At the same time, school isn't the be all and end all of your life. In fact, while you mind what your friends think, you couldn't care less about the teachers. You don't want to be friends with them but at the same time you know better than to make enemies out of them. You're the sort of girl who'll do so well they'll say, 'Goodness she was so quiet at school, who'd have thought it.'

### 75 – 100

Bit of a crawly creep aren't you? You're so busy trying to impress the teachers for the wrong reasons that you've forgotten what school is all about. It's more than work you know. Look around you, there are lots of friends to be made and lots of fun to be had. You don't have to be one of those annoying class clowns to have a good time. Lighten up a bit and enjoy the social side of school life and you'll be amazed at what it does for you.

# YOUR
## *future*

The future can be quite a scary prospect can't it?  A lot of people refuse to even think about it, while others spend so much time planning for it that they forget to enjoy the present. Yet, at the end of day, you have to remember the future isn't that far away.

When you're at school it's easy not to think about a time when you'll have to make your own decisions, be responsible for your own choices and earn money to live, eat and survive. But before I put you off, it's really nothing to be afraid of as long as you plan for it. This means deciding on a career and being positive about where you're going and what you're going to do.

If you are completely stuck for career choices then there are a number of places you can go to for help. The careers centre or a careers teacher is the first step. Go along and have a chat with them. Tell them what you want to do, and if they're good at their job they'll tell you how to go about it. Don't let them put you off or try to pin you down to a "proper" job. You can be whatever you want as long as you're realistic about it and willing to work hard. For instance, it's no good wanting to be a doctor or vet if you're no good at the Sciences.

But, don't be put off and think,

I'm good at nothing and I have no talents, therefore I won't bother to try anything. Everyone is good at something. Think about what you enjoy doing. Is it watching videos? Playing sport? Or are you good at chatting and listening to your friends? If it's videos, what about a career in that industry? There are millions of things you can do if you just investigate the right area. Likewise, sport has a hundred jobs within it, not all are just on teams. As for chatting and listening to friends, perhaps a career in the caring professions would be good for you.

Whatever you do, don't give up and settle for something you really don't want to do. Aiming high means going for something you're going to find fulfilling and not just something that is going to make you a lot of money. Remember, if you're going to take the plunge into the job market there are some pitfalls to be aware of. For a start, there is a recession on which means there aren't that many training jobs. Then if

you're 16 years old and have no qualifications, then your chances of getting a satisfying job are pretty low. Instead of ending up on a Youth Training Scheme for a pittance, why not stay at school or go to college for another year and then leave with some skills under your belt.

You don't have to make any decisions right now, and what's more you can change your mind at any time. Just have a think about it, that's all. What's more, have a chat to the people who care about you, they may have some pearls of wisdom to help you on your way. In the words of George & Artist:

'Don't be afraid to try everything. Do as much as you possibly can in one lifetime. Don't close yourself down.'

# JOB for YOU?

It can be hard to know what to aim for when you don't think you've got any talents or shine in any particular area. This quiz is designed to help you discover what areas you might be able to find a career in.

# 1 You and your friends decide to go shopping. What are you most likely to come back with?

- [ ] **a** Clothes, records and your favourite magazine.
- [ ] **b** A heap of books.
- [ ] **c** A stray dog you find in the car park.

# 2 When it comes to sport, how do you fare?

- [ ] **a** Pretty well in team games, but you hate watching others play.
- [ ] **b** You prefer things like gymnastics where you don't have to rely on others.
- [ ] **c** You love the excitement of Wimbledon and the Olympics but you're not really into doing any of it.

# 3 You're at a party and don't know many people. Where would you spend most of the night?

- [ ] **a** In the kitchen chatting to people, where it's not so noisy.
- [ ] **b** Getting down like Kylie in the middle of the dance floor.
- [ ] **c** In the corner examining the potted Yucca.

# 4 What famous woman do you most admire and why?

- [ ] **a** The model Cindy Crawford, because she's beautiful, talented and married to a famous actor.

☐ **b** Body Shop's Anita Roddick, because she launched something she believed in and made a success out of it.

☐ **c** Mother Theresa, because she is helping the Third World when no-one else is.

# 5 You see a girl from your school steal something in the supermarket. What are you likely to do?

☐ **a** Ignore it, it's none of your business.

☐ **b** Tell a shop assistant because shop-lifting puts prices up and that means you'll suffer.

☐ **c** Say nothing in the shop but speak to the girl later and see if she has a problem at home.

# 6 How would your friends best describe you?

☐ **a** Energetic and adventurous. The life and soul of a party.

☐ **b** Quiet and meticulous. Someone who is trustworthy and loyal.

☐ **c** Friendly and caring. Someone who'd always help others.

# 7 What do you do in your spare time?

☐

☐ **a** Go to concerts, shop and listen to records.

**b** Voluntary work, where you can get out and meet
☐ people.

**c** A hobby of some sort.

# 8 You're going for a work experience job, what would you wear?

**a** Something casual like jeans and a t-shirt.

**b** A smart suit, that shows you mean business.

**c** Your best gear – tight lycra leggings, and a ribbed top.

## 9 What's your favourite film?

**a** Pretty Woman.

**b** Working Girl.

**c** Parenthood.

## 10 You're in class when you suddenly burp really loudly. What do you do?

**a** Go bright red, apologise and rush out of class.

**b** Say sorry, but explain how you're allergic to your lunch.

**c** Laugh loudly, it's nothing new, you do it all the time.

**1** a 0　　b 5　　c 10

**2** a 10　　b 5　　c 0

**3** a 10　　b 0　　c 5

**4** a 0　　b 5　　c 10

**5** a 5　　b 0　　c 10

**6** a 0　　b 5　　c 10

**7** a 0　　b 10　　c 5

**8** a 10　　b 5　　c 0

**9** a 0　　b 5　　c 10

**10** a 5　　b 10　　c 0

### 0 – 30

You like the glitz and glamour of life. You know what's hip and what isn't, who's dating whom and where to hang out. A job in the media would suit you. If you aren't into the performing arts, like dancing and acting, try writing. If not, what about TV presenting, cameraman, reporter, DJ – the list is endless.

### 35 – 70

You're suited to business or a profession. Something that would keep your mind active and yet give you the prestige and security you like. If a job in high finance or a corporation doesn't suit you, then maybe a lawyer or doctor is more up your street. On the other hand, you could go into business yourself. That way you don't have to listen to anyone and you're still in business.

### 75 – 100

A job in the caring professions would suit you. It's an ideal way to use your abilities with people to their fullest advantage. A teacher, nurse, charity worker, social worker or psychologist are some of the professions you may excel at. You're also a good communicator which means you could also be good at a job in the media that has to do with people.

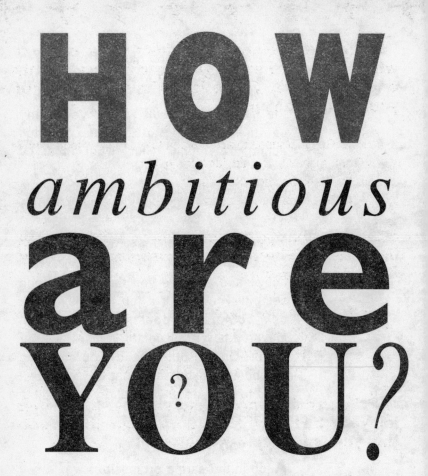

# HOW *ambitious* are YOU?

Would you 'accidentally-on-purpose' trip up your best friend to get where you wanted? Or are you more likely to lie down in a puddle to let someone get what they want? Ambition: have you got it or not? Try this quiz and find out.

## 1 You're queuing for tickets for a concert when you overhear a girl saying there is only one ticket left. There is a person in front of you. What do you do?

- [ ] **a** Get your friend to scream and faint. Then, when every one rushes to her aid, jump the queue.
- [ ] **b** Go home and sulk for days.
- [ ] **c** See if you can persuade anyone to sell you a ticket.

## 2 You hear a boy you fancy prefers your best friend. She doesn't even know he exists, what do you do?

- [ ] **a** Sob into your pillow and swear yourself into a convent.
- [ ] **b** Tell him she's engaged to this hunky boxing champion who gets extremely jealous.
- [ ] **c** Tell her and turn your attentions to his best friend.

## 3 You really want these expensive earrings for your birthday. How do you go about getting your mum to buy them?

- [ ] **a** Pretend you've lost your favourite earrings and whinge till she buys you the ones you want.
- [ ] **b** Talk very loudly on the phone to your friend about them and hope your mum overhears.
- [ ] **c** Forget about them – you're useless about being subtle.

## 4 You get lousy marks on your English test, but on your report card your teacher has given you a much higher mark by accident.

121

## Do you confess?

☐ **a** No, but you feel terribly guilty about it all term.
☐ **b** No way, in fact you boast about it.
☐ **c** Yes, you know you'll get caught in the end.

## 5 Your friend tries on a new dress for your birthday party. She looks fabulous in it but asks your opinion. What do you say?

☐ **a** 'It looks great but … your hips look massive.'
☐ **b** 'You look fab.'
☐ **c** 'It's fine.'

## 6 You're at a party and feel really shy, how are you likely to behave?

☐ **a** Take a deep breath and become the life and soul of the evening.
☐ **b** Sneak off into the corner and chat up the light fitting.
☐ **c** Talk to a few people and then go home early.

## 7 You find out your boyfriend is two timing you. What do you do?

☐ **a** Turn up at the next school disco with a male model you've hired for the night.
☐ **b** Chuck him straight away and then cry for two weeks.
☐ **c** Nothing; you hope you're wrong.

## 8 You get offered work experience at two places. How would you make your decision?

□ **a** On which one had the shortest hours.
□ **b** On how high-powered the position is.
□ **c** On how handsome the men are.

## 9 What's your idea of the perfect job?

□ **a** Something glamorous that gives you a flash office, a couple of secretaries and a designer wardrobe.
□ **b** Something that allows you to be creative, inspired and happy.
□ **c** Something well-paid with not too much stress.

## 10 You fancy a guy you see in a café. How do you get his attention?

□ **a** Walk right up to him and sit on his lap.
□ **b** Throw your coffee over him and offer to wash his shirt.
□ **c** Smile and hope he notices.

**1**  a 10  b 0  c 5

**2**  a 0  b 10  c 5

**3**  a 10  b 5  c 0

**4**  a 5  b 10  c 0

**5**  a 10  b 0  c 5

**6**  a 10  b 0  c 5

**7**  a 10  b 5  c 0

**8**  a 5  b 10  c 0

**9**  a 0  b 10  c 5

**10**  a 10  b 5  c 0

scores

### 0 – 30

Do you ever wonder why people walk all over you, take advantage of you and generally let you down? Well, it's because you let them. You need to stand up for yourself a bit more. You know there's more to life than getting ahead, but at the same time it doesn't mean you have to take everything lying down. Be braver and you'll be surprised where it gets you.

### 35 – 70

Well, you've got the balance just right you know when to be ambitious and when not to be. You know where you're going and you know how to get there. Good on you. You'll never have to worry about anyone stabbing you in the back because you'll never tread on anyone to get what you want.

### 75 – 100

You're way past ambitious, in fact I'd say you were ruthless! In business this may get you to the top of the pile but in life it will leave you at the bottom. Not everything is a competition and if you don't realise this soon, all your friends will get fed up with you. Learn to calm down a bit. You're fab enough already, you don't have to try so hard to get ahead.

125